My Pony Pals®

Address Book

Scholastic Inc.
New York   Toronto   London   Auckland   Sydney
Mexico City   New Delhi   Hong Kong

ISBN 0-439-08782-1

12 11 10 9 8 7 6 5 4 3 2   9/9 0 1 2 3 4/0

Printed in the U.S.A.   40
First Scholastic printing, August 1999

Pony Pals,

Here is your very own address, telephone, e-mail, and birthday book. With your Pony Pals Address Book handy at all times, it'll be easy to keep in touch with all your friends and relatives.

So whether it's the address of your best friend who moved across the country, the phone number of the new girl in school, or your older brother's e-mail address at college, write it all down here—and you'll never be caught without an important address or phone number again!

Keep in touch!

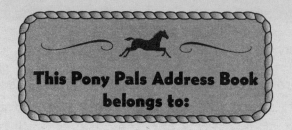

This Pony Pals Address Book
belongs to:

Name

Address

Phone number

E-mail

Birthday

♡ My Pony Pal: _____

✉ Address: _____

_____

☎ Phone number: _____

🖥 E-mail address: _____

🎁 Birthday: _____

♡ My Pony Pal: _____

✉ Address: _____

_____

☎ Phone number: _____

🖥 E-mail address: _____

🎁 Birthday: _____

♡ My Pony Pal: _____

✉ Address: _____

_____

☎ Phone number: _____

🖥 E-mail address: _____

🎁 Birthday: _____

♡ My Pony Pal: _____

✉ Address: _____

_____

☎ Phone number: _____

💻 E-mail address: _____

🎁 Birthday: _____

♡ My Pony Pal: _____

✉ Address: _____

_____

☎ Phone number: _____

💻 E-mail address: _____

🎁 Birthday: _____

♡ My Pony Pal: _____

✉ Address: _____

_____

☎ Phone number: _____

💻 E-mail address: _____

🎁 Birthday: _____

♡ My Pony Pal: _____

✉ Address: _____

_____

☎ Phone number: _____

💻 E-mail address: _____

🎁 Birthday: _____

♡ My Pony Pal: _____

✉ Address: _____

_____

☎ Phone number: _____

💻 E-mail address: _____

🎁 Birthday: _____

♡ My Pony Pal: _____

✉ Address: _____

_____

☎ Phone number: _____

💻 E-mail address: _____

🎁 Birthday: _____

♡ My Pony Pal: _____

✉ Address: _____

_____

☎ Phone number: _____

💻 E-mail address: _____

🎁 Birthday: _____

♡ My Pony Pal: _____

✉ Address: _____

_____

☎ Phone number: _____

💻 E-mail address: _____

🎁 Birthday: _____

♡ My Pony Pal: _____

✉ Address: _____

_____

☎ Phone number: _____

💻 E-mail address: _____

🎁 Birthday: _____

♡ My Pony Pal:_____

✉ Address:_____

_____

☎ Phone number:_____

🖳 E-mail address:_____

🎁 Birthday:_____

♡ My Pony Pal:_____

✉ Address:_____

_____

☎ Phone number:_____

🖳 E-mail address:_____

🎁 Birthday:_____

♡ My Pony Pal:_____

✉ Address:_____

_____

☎ Phone number:_____

🖳 E-mail address:_____

🎁 Birthday:_____

♡ My Pony Pal: _____

✉ Address: _____

_____

☎ Phone number: _____

🖥 E-mail address: _____

🎁 Birthday: _____

♡ My Pony Pal: _____

✉ Address: _____

_____

☎ Phone number: _____

🖥 E-mail address: _____

🎁 Birthday: _____

♡ My Pony Pal: _____

✉ Address: _____

_____

☎ Phone number: _____

🖥 E-mail address: _____

🎁 Birthday: _____

♡ My Pony Pal: _____

✉ Address: _____

_____

☎ Phone number: _____

🖥 E-mail address: _____

🎁 Birthday: _____

♡ My Pony Pal: _____

✉ Address: _____

_____

☎ Phone number: _____

🖥 E-mail address: _____

🎁 Birthday: _____

♡ My Pony Pal: _____

✉ Address: _____

_____

☎ Phone number: _____

🖥 E-mail address: _____

🎁 Birthday: _____

♡ My Pony Pal: _____

✉ Address: _____

_____

☎ Phone number: _____

💻 E-mail address: _____

🎁 Birthday: _____

♡ My Pony Pal: _____

✉ Address: _____

_____

☎ Phone number: _____

💻 E-mail address: _____

🎁 Birthday: _____

♡ My Pony Pal: _____

✉ Address: _____

_____

☎ Phone number: _____

💻 E-mail address: _____

🎁 Birthday: _____

♡ My Pony Pal: _____

✉ Address: _____

_____

☎ Phone number: _____

💻 E-mail address: _____

🎁 Birthday: _____

♡ My Pony Pal: _____

✉ Address: _____

_____

☎ Phone number: _____

💻 E-mail address: _____

🎁 Birthday: _____

♡ My Pony Pal: _____

✉ Address: _____

_____

☎ Phone number: _____

💻 E-mail address: _____

🎁 Birthday: _____

♡ My Pony Pal: _____

✉ Address: _____

_____

☎ Phone number: _____

💻 E-mail address: _____

🎁 Birthday: _____

♡ My Pony Pal: _____

✉ Address: _____

_____

☎ Phone number: _____

💻 E-mail address: _____

🎁 Birthday: _____

♡ My Pony Pal: _____

✉ Address: _____

_____

☎ Phone number: _____

💻 E-mail address: _____

🎁 Birthday: _____

♡ My Pony Pal: _____

✉ Address: _____

_____

☎ Phone number: _____

🖥 E-mail address: _____

🎁 Birthday: _____

♡ My Pony Pal: _____

✉ Address: _____

_____

☎ Phone number: _____

🖥 E-mail address: _____

🎁 Birthday: _____

♡ My Pony Pal: _____

✉ Address: _____

_____

☎ Phone number: _____

🖥 E-mail address: _____

🎁 Birthday: _____

♡ My Pony Pal: _____

✉ Address: _____

_____

☎ Phone number: _____

🖳 E-mail address: _____

🎁 Birthday: _____

♡ My Pony Pal: _____

✉ Address: _____

_____

☎ Phone number: _____

🖳 E-mail address: _____

🎁 Birthday: _____

♡ My Pony Pal: _____

✉ Address: _____

_____

☎ Phone number: _____

🖳 E-mail address: _____

🎁 Birthday: _____

♡ My Pony Pal: _____

✉ Address: _____

_____

☎ Phone number: _____

💻 E-mail address: _____

🎁 Birthday: _____

♡ My Pony Pal: _____

✉ Address: _____

_____

☎ Phone number: _____

💻 E-mail address: _____

🎁 Birthday: _____

♡ My Pony Pal: _____

✉ Address: _____

_____

☎ Phone number: _____

💻 E-mail address: _____

🎁 Birthday: _____

D

♡ My Pony Pal: _____

✉ Address: _____

_____

☎ Phone number: _____

💻 E-mail address: _____

🎁 Birthday: _____

♡ My Pony Pal: _____

✉ Address: _____

_____

☎ Phone number: _____

💻 E-mail address: _____

🎁 Birthday: _____

♡ My Pony Pal: _____

✉ Address: _____

_____

☎ Phone number: _____

💻 E-mail address: _____

🎁 Birthday: _____

♡ My Pony Pal:_____

✉ Address:_____

_____

☎ Phone number:_____

🖥 E-mail address:_____

🎁 Birthday:_____

♡ My Pony Pal:_____

✉ Address:_____

_____

☎ Phone number:_____

🖥 E-mail address:_____

🎁 Birthday:_____

♡ My Pony Pal:_____

✉ Address:_____

_____

☎ Phone number:_____

🖥 E-mail address:_____

🎁 Birthday:_____

♡ My Pony Pal: _____

✉ Address: _____

_____

☎ Phone number: _____

🖥 E-mail address: _____

🎁 Birthday: _____

♡ My Pony Pal: _____

✉ Address: _____

_____

☎ Phone number: _____

🖥 E-mail address: _____

🎁 Birthday: _____

♡ My Pony Pal: _____

✉ Address: _____

_____

☎ Phone number: _____

🖥 E-mail address: _____

🎁 Birthday: _____

♡ My Pony Pal: _____

✉ Address: _____

_____

☎ Phone number: _____

💻 E-mail address: _____

🎁 Birthday: _____

♡ My Pony Pal: _____

✉ Address: _____

_____

☎ Phone number: _____

💻 E-mail address: _____

🎁 Birthday: _____

♡ My Pony Pal: _____

✉ Address: _____

_____

☎ Phone number: _____

💻 E-mail address: _____

🎁 Birthday: _____

♡ My Pony Pal: _____

✉ Address: _____

_____

☎ Phone number: _____

💻 E-mail address: _____

🎁 Birthday: _____

♡ My Pony Pal: _____

✉ Address: _____

_____

☎ Phone number: _____

💻 E-mail address: _____

🎁 Birthday: _____

♡ My Pony Pal: _____

✉ Address: _____

_____

☎ Phone number: _____

💻 E-mail address: _____

🎁 Birthday: _____

♡ My Pony Pal:_____

✉ Address:_____

_____

☎ Phone number:_____

💻 E-mail address:_____

🎁 Birthday:_____

♡ My Pony Pal:_____

✉ Address:_____

_____

☎ Phone number:_____

💻 E-mail address:_____

🎁 Birthday:_____

♡ My Pony Pal:_____

✉ Address:_____

_____

☎ Phone number:_____

💻 E-mail address:_____

🎁 Birthday:_____

♡ My Pony Pal: _____

✉ Address: _____

_____

☎ Phone number: _____

💻 E-mail address: _____

🎁 Birthday: _____

♡ My Pony Pal: _____

✉ Address: _____

_____

☎ Phone number: _____

💻 E-mail address: _____

🎁 Birthday: _____

♡ My Pony Pal: _____

✉ Address: _____

_____

☎ Phone number: _____

💻 E-mail address: _____

🎁 Birthday: _____

♡ My Pony Pal: _____

✉ Address: _____

_____

☎ Phone number: _____

🖥 E-mail address: _____

🎁 Birthday: _____

♡ My Pony Pal: _____

✉ Address: _____

_____

☎ Phone number: _____

🖥 E-mail address: _____

🎁 Birthday: _____

♡ My Pony Pal: _____

✉ Address: _____

_____

☎ Phone number: _____

🖥 E-mail address: _____

🎁 Birthday: _____

♡ My Pony Pal: _____

✉ Address: _____

_____

☎ Phone number: _____

💻 E-mail address: _____

🎁 Birthday: _____

♡ My Pony Pal: _____

✉ Address: _____

_____

☎ Phone number: _____

💻 E-mail address: _____

🎁 Birthday: _____

♡ My Pony Pal: _____

✉ Address: _____

_____

☎ Phone number: _____

💻 E-mail address: _____

🎁 Birthday: _____

♡ My Pony Pal: _____

✉ Address: _____

_____

☎ Phone number: _____

🖥 E-mail address: _____

🎁 Birthday: _____

♡ My Pony Pal: _____

✉ Address: _____

_____

☎ Phone number: _____

🖥 E-mail address: _____

🎁 Birthday: _____

♡ My Pony Pal: _____

✉ Address: _____

_____

☎ Phone number: _____

🖥 E-mail address: _____

🎁 Birthday: _____

♡ My Pony Pal:_____

✉ Address:_____

_____

☎ Phone number:_____

💻 E-mail address:_____

🎁 Birthday:_____

♡ My Pony Pal:_____

✉ Address:_____

_____

☎ Phone number:_____

💻 E-mail address:_____

🎁 Birthday:_____

♡ My Pony Pal:_____

✉ Address:_____

_____

☎ Phone number:_____

💻 E-mail address:_____

🎁 Birthday:_____

♡ My Pony Pal: _____

✉ Address: _____

_____

☎ Phone number: _____

🖥 E-mail address: _____

🎁 Birthday: _____

♡ My Pony Pal: _____

✉ Address: _____

_____

☎ Phone number: _____

🖥 E-mail address: _____

🎁 Birthday: _____

♡ My Pony Pal: _____

✉ Address: _____

_____

☎ Phone number: _____

🖥 E-mail address: _____

🎁 Birthday: _____

♡ My Pony Pal: _____

✉ Address: _____

_____

☎ Phone number: _____

🖥 E-mail address: _____

🎁 Birthday: _____

♡ My Pony Pal: _____

✉ Address: _____

_____

☎ Phone number: _____

🖥 E-mail address: _____

🎁 Birthday: _____

♡ My Pony Pal: _____

✉ Address: _____

_____

☎ Phone number: _____

🖥 E-mail address: _____

🎁 Birthday: _____

♡ My Pony Pal: _____

✉ Address: _____

_____

☎ Phone number: _____

💻 E-mail address: _____

🎁 Birthday: _____

♡ My Pony Pal: _____

✉ Address: _____

_____

☎ Phone number: _____

💻 E-mail address: _____

🎁 Birthday: _____

♡ My Pony Pal: _____

✉ Address: _____

_____

☎ Phone number: _____

💻 E-mail address: _____

🎁 Birthday: _____

♡ My Pony Pal: _____

✉ Address: _____

_____

☎ Phone number: _____

💻 E-mail address: _____

🎁 Birthday: _____

♡ My Pony Pal: _____

✉ Address: _____

_____

☎ Phone number: _____

💻 E-mail address: _____

🎁 Birthday: _____

♡ My Pony Pal: _____

✉ Address: _____

_____

☎ Phone number: _____

💻 E-mail address: _____

🎁 Birthday: _____

♡ My Pony Pal: _____

✉ Address: _____

_____

☎ Phone number: _____

🖥 E-mail address: _____

🎁 Birthday: _____

♡ My Pony Pal: _____

✉ Address: _____

_____

☎ Phone number: _____

🖥 E-mail address: _____

🎁 Birthday: _____

♡ My Pony Pal: _____

✉ Address: _____

_____

☎ Phone number: _____

🖥 E-mail address: _____

🎁 Birthday: _____

♡ My Pony Pal: _____

✉ Address: _____

_____

☎ Phone number: _____

🖥 E-mail address: _____

🎁 Birthday: _____

♡ My Pony Pal: _____

✉ Address: _____

_____

☎ Phone number: _____

🖥 E-mail address: _____

🎁 Birthday: _____

♡ My Pony Pal: _____

✉ Address: _____

_____

☎ Phone number: _____

🖥 E-mail address: _____

🎁 Birthday: _____

♡ My Pony Pal: _____

✉ Address: _____

_____

☎ Phone number: _____

💻 E-mail address: _____

🎁 Birthday: _____

♡ My Pony Pal: _____

✉ Address: _____

_____

☎ Phone number: _____

💻 E-mail address: _____

🎁 Birthday: _____

♡ My Pony Pal: _____

✉ Address: _____

_____

☎ Phone number: _____

💻 E-mail address: _____

🎁 Birthday: _____

♡ My Pony Pal: _____

✉ Address: _____

_____

☎ Phone number: _____

💻 E-mail address: _____

🎁 Birthday: _____

♡ My Pony Pal: _____

✉ Address: _____

_____

☎ Phone number: _____

💻 E-mail address: _____

🎁 Birthday: _____

♡ My Pony Pal: _____

✉ Address: _____

_____

☎ Phone number: _____

💻 E-mail address: _____

🎁 Birthday: _____

♡ My Pony Pal: _____

✉ Address: _____

_____

☎ Phone number: _____

🖥 E-mail address: _____

🎁 Birthday: _____

♡ My Pony Pal: _____

✉ Address: _____

_____

☎ Phone number: _____

🖥 E-mail address: _____

🎁 Birthday: _____

♡ My Pony Pal: _____

✉ Address: _____

_____

☎ Phone number: _____

🖥 E-mail address: _____

🎁 Birthday: _____

♡ My Pony Pal: _____

✉ Address: _____

_____

☎ Phone number: _____

🖳 E-mail address: _____

🎁 Birthday: _____

♡ My Pony Pal: _____

✉ Address: _____

_____

☎ Phone number: _____

🖳 E-mail address: _____

🎁 Birthday: _____

♡ My Pony Pal: _____

✉ Address: _____

_____

☎ Phone number: _____

🖳 E-mail address: _____

🎁 Birthday: _____

♡ My Pony Pal: _____

✉ Address: _____

_____

☎ Phone number: _____

💻 E-mail address: _____

🎁 Birthday: _____

♡ My Pony Pal: _____

✉ Address: _____

_____

☎ Phone number: _____

💻 E-mail address: _____

🎁 Birthday: _____

♡ My Pony Pal: _____

✉ Address: _____

_____

☎ Phone number: _____

💻 E-mail address: _____

🎁 Birthday: _____

♡ My Pony Pal: _____

✉ Address: _____

_____

☎ Phone number: _____

🖥 E-mail address: _____

🎁 Birthday: _____

♡ My Pony Pal: _____

✉ Address: _____

_____

☎ Phone number: _____

🖥 E-mail address: _____

🎁 Birthday: _____

♡ My Pony Pal: _____

✉ Address: _____

_____

☎ Phone number: _____

🖥 E-mail address: _____

🎁 Birthday: _____

♡ My Pony Pal: _____

✉ Address: _____

_____

☎ Phone number: _____

🖥 E-mail address: _____

🎁 Birthday: _____

♡ My Pony Pal: _____

✉ Address: _____

_____

☎ Phone number: _____

🖥 E-mail address: _____

🎁 Birthday: _____

♡ My Pony Pal: _____

✉ Address: _____

_____

☎ Phone number: _____

🖥 E-mail address: _____

🎁 Birthday: _____

J

♡ My Pony Pal: _____

✉ Address: _____

_____

☎ Phone number: _____

💻 E-mail address: _____

🎁 Birthday: _____

♡ My Pony Pal: _____

✉ Address: _____

_____

☎ Phone number: _____

💻 E-mail address: _____

🎁 Birthday: _____

♡ My Pony Pal: _____

✉ Address: _____

_____

☎ Phone number: _____

💻 E-mail address: _____

🎁 Birthday: _____

♡ My Pony Pal: _____

✉ Address: _____

_____

☎ Phone number: _____

🖥 E-mail address: _____

🎁 Birthday: _____

♡ My Pony Pal: _____

✉ Address: _____

_____

☎ Phone number: _____

🖥 E-mail address: _____

🎁 Birthday: _____

♡ My Pony Pal: _____

✉ Address: _____

_____

☎ Phone number: _____

🖥 E-mail address: _____

🎁 Birthday: _____

♡ My Pony Pal: _____

✉ Address: _____

_____

☎ Phone number: _____

🖥 E-mail address: _____

🎁 Birthday: _____

♡ My Pony Pal: _____

✉ Address: _____

_____

☎ Phone number: _____

🖥 E-mail address: _____

🎁 Birthday: _____

♡ My Pony Pal: _____

✉ Address: _____

_____

☎ Phone number: _____

🖥 E-mail address: _____

🎁 Birthday: _____

♡ My Pony Pal:_____

✉ Address:_____

_____

☎ Phone number:_____

💻 E-mail address:_____

🎁 Birthday:_____

♡ My Pony Pal:_____

✉ Address:_____

_____

☎ Phone number:_____

💻 E-mail address:_____

🎁 Birthday:_____

♡ My Pony Pal:_____

✉ Address:_____

_____

☎ Phone number:_____

💻 E-mail address:_____

🎁 Birthday:_____

♡ My Pony Pal: _____

✉ Address: _____

_____

☎ Phone number: _____

💻 E-mail address: _____

🎁 Birthday: _____

♡ My Pony Pal: _____

✉ Address: _____

_____

☎ Phone number: _____

💻 E-mail address: _____

🎁 Birthday: _____

♡ My Pony Pal: _____

✉ Address: _____

_____

☎ Phone number: _____

💻 E-mail address: _____

🎁 Birthday: _____

♡ My Pony Pal: _____

✉ Address: _____

_____

☎ Phone number: _____

💻 E-mail address: _____

🎁 Birthday: _____

♡ My Pony Pal: _____

✉ Address: _____

_____

☎ Phone number: _____

💻 E-mail address: _____

🎁 Birthday: _____

♡ My Pony Pal: _____

✉ Address: _____

_____

☎ Phone number: _____

💻 E-mail address: _____

🎁 Birthday: _____

K

♡ My Pony Pal: _____

✉ Address: _____

_____

☎ Phone number: _____

💻 E-mail address: _____

🎁 Birthday: _____

♡ My Pony Pal: _____

✉ Address: _____

_____

☎ Phone number: _____

💻 E-mail address: _____

🎁 Birthday: _____

♡ My Pony Pal: _____

✉ Address: _____

_____

☎ Phone number: _____

💻 E-mail address: _____

🎁 Birthday: _____

♡ My Pony Pal: _____

✉ Address: _____

_____

☎ Phone number: _____

🖥 E-mail address: _____

🎁 Birthday: _____

♡ My Pony Pal: _____

✉ Address: _____

_____

☎ Phone number: _____

🖥 E-mail address: _____

🎁 Birthday: _____

♡ My Pony Pal: _____

✉ Address: _____

_____

☎ Phone number: _____

🖥 E-mail address: _____

🎁 Birthday: _____

♡ My Pony Pal: _____

✉ Address: _____

_____

☎ Phone number: _____

💻 E-mail address: _____

🎁 Birthday: _____

♡ My Pony Pal: _____

✉ Address: _____

_____

☎ Phone number: _____

💻 E-mail address: _____

🎁 Birthday: _____

♡ My Pony Pal: _____

✉ Address: _____

_____

☎ Phone number: _____

💻 E-mail address: _____

🎁 Birthday: _____

♡ My Pony Pal: _____

✉ Address: _____

_____

☎ Phone number: _____

🖥 E-mail address: _____

🎁 Birthday: _____

♡ My Pony Pal: _____

✉ Address: _____

_____

☎ Phone number: _____

🖥 E-mail address: _____

🎁 Birthday: _____

♡ My Pony Pal: _____

✉ Address: _____

_____

☎ Phone number: _____

🖥 E-mail address: _____

🎁 Birthday: _____

♡ My Pony Pal: _____

✉ Address: _____

_____

☎ Phone number: _____

🖥 E-mail address: _____

🎁 Birthday: _____

♡ My Pony Pal: _____

✉ Address: _____

_____

☎ Phone number: _____

🖥 E-mail address: _____

🎁 Birthday: _____

♡ My Pony Pal: _____

✉ Address: _____

_____

☎ Phone number: _____

🖥 E-mail address: _____

🎁 Birthday: _____

♡ My Pony Pal: _____

✉ Address: _____

_____

☎ Phone number: _____

💻 E-mail address: _____

🎁 Birthday: _____

♡ My Pony Pal: _____

✉ Address: _____

_____

☎ Phone number: _____

💻 E-mail address: _____

🎁 Birthday: _____

♡ My Pony Pal: _____

✉ Address: _____

_____

☎ Phone number: _____

💻 E-mail address: _____

🎁 Birthday: _____

♡ My Pony Pal: _____

✉ Address: _____

_____

☎ Phone number: _____

🖥 E-mail address: _____

🎁 Birthday: _____

♡ My Pony Pal: _____

✉ Address: _____

_____

☎ Phone number: _____

🖥 E-mail address: _____

🎁 Birthday: _____

♡ My Pony Pal: _____

✉ Address: _____

_____

☎ Phone number: _____

🖥 E-mail address: _____

🎁 Birthday: _____

♡ My Pony Pal: _____

✉ Address: _____

_____

☎ Phone number: _____

💻 E-mail address: _____

🎁 Birthday: _____

♡ My Pony Pal: _____

✉ Address: _____

_____

☎ Phone number: _____

💻 E-mail address: _____

🎁 Birthday: _____

♡ My Pony Pal: _____

✉ Address: _____

_____

☎ Phone number: _____

💻 E-mail address: _____

🎁 Birthday: _____

M

♡ My Pony Pal: _____

✉ Address: _____

_____

☏ Phone number: _____

🖳 E-mail address: _____

🎁 Birthday: _____

♡ My Pony Pal: _____

✉ Address: _____

_____

☏ Phone number: _____

🖳 E-mail address: _____

🎁 Birthday: _____

♡ My Pony Pal: _____

✉ Address: _____

_____

☏ Phone number: _____

🖳 E-mail address: _____

🎁 Birthday: _____

♡ My Pony Pal: _____

✉ Address: _____

_____

☎ Phone number: _____

💻 E-mail address: _____

🎁 Birthday: _____

♡ My Pony Pal: _____

✉ Address: _____

_____

☎ Phone number: _____

💻 E-mail address: _____

🎁 Birthday: _____

♡ My Pony Pal: _____

✉ Address: _____

_____

☎ Phone number: _____

💻 E-mail address: _____

🎁 Birthday: _____

♡ My Pony Pal: _____

✉ Address: _____

_____

☎ Phone number: _____

💻 E-mail address: _____

🎁 Birthday: _____

♡ My Pony Pal: _____

✉ Address: _____

_____

☎ Phone number: _____

💻 E-mail address: _____

🎁 Birthday: _____

♡ My Pony Pal: _____

✉ Address: _____

_____

☎ Phone number: _____

💻 E-mail address: _____

🎁 Birthday: _____

♡ My Pony Pal:_____

✉ Address:_____

_____

☎ Phone number:_____

💻 E-mail address:_____

🎁 Birthday:_____

♡ My Pony Pal:_____

✉ Address:_____

_____

☎ Phone number:_____

💻 E-mail address:_____

🎁 Birthday:_____

♡ My Pony Pal:_____

✉ Address:_____

_____

☎ Phone number:_____

💻 E-mail address:_____

🎁 Birthday:_____

♡ My Pony Pal: _____

✉ Address: _____

_____

☎ Phone number: _____

🖥 E-mail address: _____

🎁 Birthday: _____

♡ My Pony Pal: _____

✉ Address: _____

_____

☎ Phone number: _____

🖥 E-mail address: _____

🎁 Birthday: _____

♡ My Pony Pal: _____

✉ Address: _____

_____

☎ Phone number: _____

🖥 E-mail address: _____

🎁 Birthday: _____

♡ My Pony Pal: _____

✉ Address: _____

_____

☎ Phone number: _____

💻 E-mail address: _____

🎁 Birthday: _____

♡ My Pony Pal: _____

✉ Address: _____

_____

☎ Phone number: _____

💻 E-mail address: _____

🎁 Birthday: _____

♡ My Pony Pal: _____

✉ Address: _____

_____

☎ Phone number: _____

💻 E-mail address: _____

🎁 Birthday: _____

♡ My Pony Pal: _____

✉ Address: _____

_____

☎ Phone number: _____

💻 E-mail address: _____

🎁 Birthday: _____

♡ My Pony Pal: _____

✉ Address: _____

_____

☎ Phone number: _____

💻 E-mail address: _____

🎁 Birthday: _____

♡ My Pony Pal: _____

✉ Address: _____

_____

☎ Phone number: _____

💻 E-mail address: _____

🎁 Birthday: _____

♡ My Pony Pal: _____

✉ Address: _____

_____

☎ Phone number: _____

💻 E-mail address: _____

🎁 Birthday: _____

♡ My Pony Pal: _____

✉ Address: _____

_____

☎ Phone number: _____

💻 E-mail address: _____

🎁 Birthday: _____

♡ My Pony Pal: _____

✉ Address: _____

_____

☎ Phone number: _____

💻 E-mail address: _____

🎁 Birthday: _____

♡ My Pony Pal:_____

✉ Address:_____

_____

☎ Phone number:_____

💻 E-mail address:_____

🎁 Birthday:_____

♡ My Pony Pal:_____

✉ Address:_____

_____

☎ Phone number:_____

💻 E-mail address:_____

🎁 Birthday:_____

♡ My Pony Pal:_____

✉ Address:_____

_____

☎ Phone number:_____

💻 E-mail address:_____

🎁 Birthday:_____

♡ My Pony Pal: _____

✉ Address: _____

_____

☎ Phone number: _____

🖥 E-mail address: _____

🎁 Birthday: _____

♡ My Pony Pal: _____

✉ Address: _____

_____

☎ Phone number: _____

🖥 E-mail address: _____

🎁 Birthday: _____

♡ My Pony Pal: _____

✉ Address: _____

_____

☎ Phone number: _____

🖥 E-mail address: _____

🎁 Birthday: _____

♡ My Pony Pal: _____

✉ Address: _____

_____

☎ Phone number: _____

💻 E-mail address: _____

🎁 Birthday: _____

♡ My Pony Pal: _____

✉ Address: _____

_____

☎ Phone number: _____

💻 E-mail address: _____

🎁 Birthday: _____

♡ My Pony Pal: _____

✉ Address: _____

_____

☎ Phone number: _____

💻 E-mail address: _____

🎁 Birthday: _____

♡ My Pony Pal: _____

✉ Address: _____

_____

☎ Phone number: _____

💻 E-mail address: _____

🎁 Birthday: _____

♡ My Pony Pal: _____

✉ Address: _____

_____

☎ Phone number: _____

💻 E-mail address: _____

🎁 Birthday: _____

♡ My Pony Pal: _____

✉ Address: _____

_____

☎ Phone number: _____

💻 E-mail address: _____

🎁 Birthday: _____

♡ My Pony Pal: _____

✉ Address: _____

_____

☎ Phone number: _____

💻 E-mail address: _____

🎁 Birthday: _____

♡ My Pony Pal: _____

✉ Address: _____

_____

☎ Phone number: _____

💻 E-mail address: _____

🎁 Birthday: _____

♡ My Pony Pal: _____

✉ Address: _____

_____

☎ Phone number: _____

💻 E-mail address: _____

🎁 Birthday: _____

♡ My Pony Pal: _____

✉ Address: _____

_____

☎ Phone number: _____

💻 E-mail address: _____

🎁 Birthday: _____

♡ My Pony Pal: _____

✉ Address: _____

_____

☎ Phone number: _____

💻 E-mail address: _____

🎁 Birthday: _____

♡ My Pony Pal: _____

✉ Address: _____

_____

☎ Phone number: _____

💻 E-mail address: _____

🎁 Birthday: _____

♡ My Pony Pal: _____

✉ Address: _____

_____

☎ Phone number: _____

💻 E-mail address: _____

🎁 Birthday: _____

♡ My Pony Pal: _____

✉ Address: _____

_____

☎ Phone number: _____

💻 E-mail address: _____

🎁 Birthday: _____

♡ My Pony Pal: _____

✉ Address: _____

_____

☎ Phone number: _____

💻 E-mail address: _____

🎁 Birthday: _____

♡ My Pony Pal: _____

✉ Address: _____

_____

☎ Phone number: _____

💻 E-mail address: _____

🎁 Birthday: _____

♡ My Pony Pal: _____

✉ Address: _____

_____

☎ Phone number: _____

💻 E-mail address: _____

🎁 Birthday: _____

♡ My Pony Pal: _____

✉ Address: _____

_____

☎ Phone number: _____

💻 E-mail address: _____

🎁 Birthday: _____

♡ My Pony Pal: _____

✉ Address: _____

_____

☎ Phone number: _____

💻 E-mail address: _____

🎁 Birthday: _____

♡ My Pony Pal: _____

✉ Address: _____

_____

☎ Phone number: _____

💻 E-mail address: _____

🎁 Birthday: _____

♡ My Pony Pal: _____

✉ Address: _____

_____

☎ Phone number: _____

💻 E-mail address: _____

🎁 Birthday: _____

♡ My Pony Pal:_____

✉ Address:_____

_____

☏ Phone number:_____

🖥 E-mail address:_____

🎁 Birthday:_____

♡ My Pony Pal:_____

✉ Address:_____

_____

☏ Phone number:_____

🖥 E-mail address:_____

🎁 Birthday:_____

♡ My Pony Pal:_____

✉ Address:_____

_____

☏ Phone number:_____

🖥 E-mail address:_____

🎁 Birthday:_____

♡ My Pony Pal: _____

✉ Address: _____

_____

☎ Phone number: _____

💻 E-mail address: _____

🎁 Birthday: _____

♡ My Pony Pal: _____

✉ Address: _____

_____

☎ Phone number: _____

💻 E-mail address: _____

🎁 Birthday: _____

♡ My Pony Pal: _____

✉ Address: _____

_____

☎ Phone number: _____

💻 E-mail address: _____

🎁 Birthday: _____

♡ My Pony Pal: _____

✉ Address: _____

_____

☎ Phone number: _____

🖥 E-mail address: _____

🎁 Birthday: _____

♡ My Pony Pal: _____

✉ Address: _____

_____

☎ Phone number: _____

🖥 E-mail address: _____

🎁 Birthday: _____

♡ My Pony Pal: _____

✉ Address: _____

_____

☎ Phone number: _____

🖥 E-mail address: _____

🎁 Birthday: _____

♡ My Pony Pal: _____

✉ Address: _____

_____

☎ Phone number: _____

💻 E-mail address: _____

🎁 Birthday: _____

♡ My Pony Pal: _____

✉ Address: _____

_____

☎ Phone number: _____

💻 E-mail address: _____

🎁 Birthday: _____

♡ My Pony Pal: _____

✉ Address: _____

_____

☎ Phone number: _____

💻 E-mail address: _____

🎁 Birthday: _____

♡ My Pony Pal: _____

✉ Address: _____

_____

☎ Phone number: _____

💻 E-mail address: _____

🎁 Birthday: _____

♡ My Pony Pal: _____

✉ Address: _____

_____

☎ Phone number: _____

💻 E-mail address: _____

🎁 Birthday: _____

♡ My Pony Pal: _____

✉ Address: _____

_____

☎ Phone number: _____

💻 E-mail address: _____

🎁 Birthday: _____

♡ My Pony Pal: _____

✉ Address: _____

_____

☎ Phone number: _____

💻 E-mail address: _____

🎁 Birthday: _____

♡ My Pony Pal: _____

✉ Address: _____

_____

☎ Phone number: _____

💻 E-mail address: _____

🎁 Birthday: _____

♡ My Pony Pal: _____

✉ Address: _____

_____

☎ Phone number: _____

💻 E-mail address: _____

🎁 Birthday: _____

♡ My Pony Pal: _____

✉ Address: _____

_____

☎ Phone number: _____

🖳 E-mail address: _____

🎁 Birthday: _____

♡ My Pony Pal: _____

✉ Address: _____

_____

☎ Phone number: _____

🖳 E-mail address: _____

🎁 Birthday: _____

♡ My Pony Pal: _____

✉ Address: _____

_____

☎ Phone number: _____

🖳 E-mail address: _____

🎁 Birthday: _____

♡ My Pony Pal: _____

✉ Address: _____

_____

☎ Phone number: _____

🖥 E-mail address: _____

🎁 Birthday: _____

♡ My Pony Pal: _____

✉ Address: _____

_____

☎ Phone number: _____

🖥 E-mail address: _____

🎁 Birthday: _____

♡ My Pony Pal: _____

✉ Address: _____

_____

☎ Phone number: _____

🖥 E-mail address: _____

🎁 Birthday: _____

♡ My Pony Pal: _____

✉ Address: _____

_____

☎ Phone number: _____

💻 E-mail address: _____

🎁 Birthday: _____

♡ My Pony Pal: _____

✉ Address: _____

_____

☎ Phone number: _____

💻 E-mail address: _____

🎁 Birthday: _____

♡ My Pony Pal: _____

✉ Address: _____

_____

☎ Phone number: _____

💻 E-mail address: _____

🎁 Birthday: _____

♡ My Pony Pal: _____

✉ Address: _____

_____

☎ Phone number: _____

💻 E-mail address: _____

🎁 Birthday: _____

♡ My Pony Pal: _____

✉ Address: _____

_____

☎ Phone number: _____

💻 E-mail address: _____

🎁 Birthday: _____

♡ My Pony Pal: _____

✉ Address: _____

_____

☎ Phone number: _____

💻 E-mail address: _____

🎁 Birthday: _____

♡ My Pony Pal:_____

✉ Address:_____

_____

☎ Phone number:_____

🖥 E-mail address:_____

🎁 Birthday:_____

♡ My Pony Pal:_____

✉ Address:_____

_____

☎ Phone number:_____

🖥 E-mail address:_____

🎁 Birthday:_____

♡ My Pony Pal:_____

✉ Address:_____

_____

☎ Phone number:_____

🖥 E-mail address:_____

🎁 Birthday:_____

♡ My Pony Pal: _____

✉ Address: _____

_____

☎ Phone number: _____

🖥 E-mail address: _____

🎁 Birthday: _____

♡ My Pony Pal: _____

✉ Address: _____

_____

☎ Phone number: _____

🖥 E-mail address: _____

🎁 Birthday: _____

♡ My Pony Pal: _____

✉ Address: _____

_____

☎ Phone number: _____

🖥 E-mail address: _____

🎁 Birthday: _____

♡ My Pony Pal: _____

✉ Address: _____

_____

☎ Phone number: _____

🖥 E-mail address: _____

🎁 Birthday: _____

♡ My Pony Pal: _____

✉ Address: _____

_____

☎ Phone number: _____

🖥 E-mail address: _____

🎁 Birthday: _____

♡ My Pony Pal: _____

✉ Address: _____

_____

☎ Phone number: _____

🖥 E-mail address: _____

🎁 Birthday: _____

♡ My Pony Pal: _____

✉ Address: _____

_____

☎ Phone number: _____

🖥 E-mail address: _____

🎁 Birthday: _____

♡ My Pony Pal: _____

✉ Address: _____

_____

☎ Phone number: _____

🖥 E-mail address: _____

🎁 Birthday: _____

♡ My Pony Pal: _____

✉ Address: _____

_____

☎ Phone number: _____

🖥 E-mail address: _____

🎁 Birthday: _____

♡ My Pony Pal: _____

✉ Address: _____

_____

☎ Phone number: _____

🖥 E-mail address: _____

🎁 Birthday: _____

♡ My Pony Pal: _____

✉ Address: _____

_____

☎ Phone number: _____

🖥 E-mail address: _____

🎁 Birthday: _____

♡ My Pony Pal: _____

✉ Address: _____

_____

☎ Phone number: _____

🖥 E-mail address: _____

🎁 Birthday: _____

♡ My Pony Pal: _____

✉ Address: _____

_____

☎ Phone number: _____

💻 E-mail address: _____

🎁 Birthday: _____

♡ My Pony Pal: _____

✉ Address: _____

_____

☎ Phone number: _____

💻 E-mail address: _____

🎁 Birthday: _____

♡ My Pony Pal: _____

✉ Address: _____

_____

☎ Phone number: _____

💻 E-mail address: _____

🎁 Birthday: _____

♡ My Pony Pal: _____

✉ Address: _____

_____

☎ Phone number: _____

🖥 E-mail address: _____

🎁 Birthday: _____

♡ My Pony Pal: _____

✉ Address: _____

_____

☎ Phone number: _____

🖥 E-mail address: _____

🎁 Birthday: _____

♡ My Pony Pal: _____

✉ Address: _____

_____

☎ Phone number: _____

🖥 E-mail address: _____

🎁 Birthday: _____

♡ My Pony Pal: _____

✉ Address: _____

_____

☎ Phone number: _____

💻 E-mail address: _____

🎁 Birthday: _____

♡ My Pony Pal: _____

✉ Address: _____

_____

☎ Phone number: _____

💻 E-mail address: _____

🎁 Birthday: _____

♡ My Pony Pal: _____

✉ Address: _____

_____

☎ Phone number: _____

💻 E-mail address: _____

🎁 Birthday: _____

♡ My Pony Pal: _____

✉ Address: _____

_____

☎ Phone number: _____

🖥 E-mail address: _____

🎁 Birthday: _____

♡ My Pony Pal: _____

✉ Address: _____

_____

☎ Phone number: _____

🖥 E-mail address: _____

🎁 Birthday: _____

♡ My Pony Pal: _____

✉ Address: _____

_____

☎ Phone number: _____

🖥 E-mail address: _____

🎁 Birthday: _____

♡ My Pony Pal: _____

✉ Address: _____

_____

☎ Phone number: _____

🖥 E-mail address: _____

🎁 Birthday: _____

♡ My Pony Pal: _____

✉ Address: _____

_____

☎ Phone number: _____

🖥 E-mail address: _____

🎁 Birthday: _____

♡ My Pony Pal: _____

✉ Address: _____

_____

☎ Phone number: _____

🖥 E-mail address: _____

🎁 Birthday: _____

♡ My Pony Pal: _____

✉ Address: _____

_____

☎ Phone number: _____

🖳 E-mail address: _____

🎁 Birthday: _____

♡ My Pony Pal: _____

✉ Address: _____

_____

☎ Phone number: _____

🖳 E-mail address: _____

🎁 Birthday: _____

♡ My Pony Pal: _____

✉ Address: _____

_____

☎ Phone number: _____

🖳 E-mail address: _____

🎁 Birthday: _____

X
Y
Z

♡ My Pony Pal:_____

✉ Address:_____

_____

☎ Phone number:_____

💻 E-mail address:_____

🎁 Birthday:_____

♡ My Pony Pal:_____

✉ Address:_____

_____

☎ Phone number:_____

💻 E-mail address:_____

🎁 Birthday:_____

♡ My Pony Pal:_____

✉ Address:_____

_____

☎ Phone number:_____

💻 E-mail address:_____

🎁 Birthday:_____

♡ My Pony Pal: _____

✉ Address: _____

_____

☎ Phone number: _____

💻 E-mail address: _____

🎁 Birthday: _____

♡ My Pony Pal: _____

✉ Address: _____

_____

☎ Phone number: _____

💻 E-mail address: _____

🎁 Birthday: _____

♡ My Pony Pal: _____

✉ Address: _____

_____

☎ Phone number: _____

💻 E-mail address: _____

🎁 Birthday: _____

X
Y
Z

♡ My Pony Pal: _____

✉ Address: _____

_____

☎ Phone number: _____

💻 E-mail address: _____

🎁 Birthday: _____

♡ My Pony Pal: _____

✉ Address: _____

_____

☎ Phone number: _____

💻 E-mail address: _____

🎁 Birthday: _____

♡ My Pony Pal: _____

✉ Address: _____

_____

☎ Phone number: _____

💻 E-mail address: _____

🎁 Birthday: _____